# Freddy Finds God

## A story of meaning and purpose

written by JOE CARUSO

illustrated by ALINA SHABELNYK

**Freddy Finds God**

Scripture taken from THE HOLY BIBLE, NEW INTERNATIONAL VERSION®, NIV® Copyright © 1973, 1978, 1984, 2011 by Biblica, Inc.™ Used by permission.
All rights reserved worldwide.

For information contact:

www.JoeCarusoStories.com

JoeCarusoStories@gmail.com

Written by: Joe Caruso

Illustrated by: Alina Shabelnyk

ISBN: 978-1-7773231-0-3 (paperback)

ISBN: 978-1-7773231-1-0 (eBook)

ISBN: 978-1-7773231-2-7 (hardcover)

Library and Archives Canada Cataloguing in Publication

Printed in the United States of America

First Edition: 2020

To Arya and J,
May you find and serve God.


Special thanks to my brother Mike,
for his guidance and support.

Freddy woke up one morning with a BIG idea. He was going to find God.

He said to his mother, "I'm going to find God today, so I can serve Him."

"That's a GREAT thing to do, Freddy," smiled his mother.

She packed him a lunch and said, "Just be home by dinner."

Freddy put on his jacket, took his lunch and off he went.

Freddy was going to find God today, so he could serve Him!

As Freddy left home he thought, "But where would God be? Maybe He's on top of the hill overlooking our neighbourhood. That would be a good place for God to be."

It was a long hike up the hill, but Freddy made it right to the top. He could see his whole neighbourhood!

But he couldn't find God.

So Freddy walked back down the hill, and along the way he met...

a boy!

"Hi! I'm Freddy," he said. "I haven't seen you around here."

"I'm Leo," the boy replied, "I just moved down the street. Do you want to play?"

Leo and Freddy threw sticks into the stream, spotted fish in the shallows, and climbed a tree right to the top.

Finally, they lay on their backs and watched the clouds.

After a while Freddy said to Leo, "I have to go now. I'm going to find God today, so I can serve Him."

As Freddy continued his journey he thought, "Where else could God be? Maybe He's in the forest with all the animals."

So off he went into the forest, where he saw...

squirrels, rabbits, birds and even a deer.

But he didn't see God.

So Freddy left the forest, and on his way out he met...

his friend Sally!

"Hi, Sally. Are you okay?" asked Freddy.

"No," she shivered. "I was playing in the park, but I'm getting cold and not feeling well."

"You can wear my jacket, Sally. Would you like me to walk you home?"

"Oh, thank you Freddy," said Sally.

After Freddy walked Sally home he said, "I have to go now, I'm going to find God today, so I can serve Him."

So off Freddy went in search of God again. But where could God be? Freddy couldn't find Him on the hill and didn't see Him in the forest.

"I know!" thought Freddy. "God must be in the city! There are lots of people in the city."

So to the city he went.

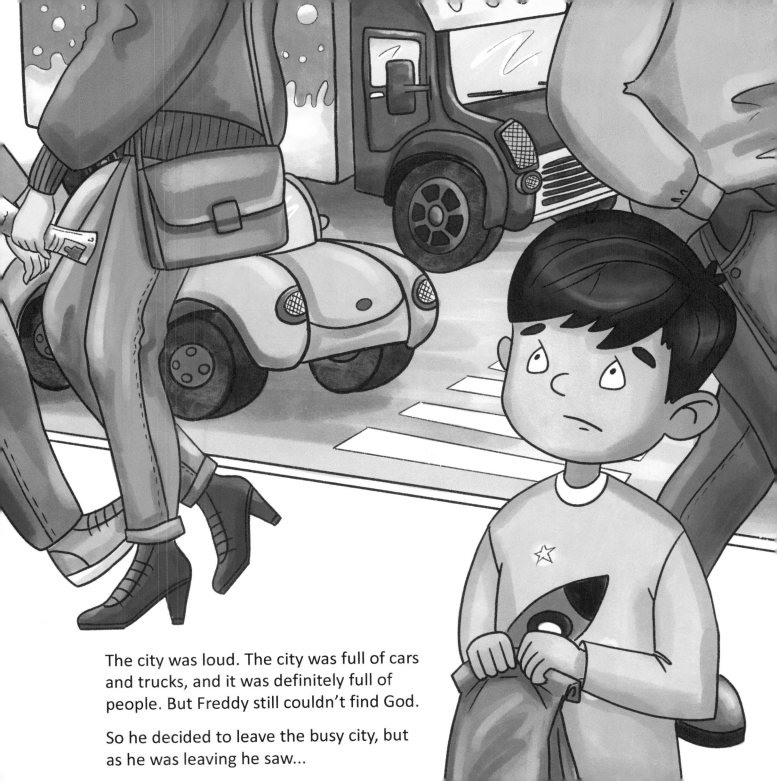

The city was loud. The city was full of cars and trucks, and it was definitely full of people. But Freddy still couldn't find God.

So he decided to leave the busy city, but as he was leaving he saw...

a man.

"Hi there, my name is Freddy. Do you need any help?" Freddy asked.

"Well hello Freddy, my name's Jim. I've been sitting here for a while and it's been a long time since I've had something to eat."

"Would you like to have my lunch?" offered Freddy.

"Oh, I couldn't do that," said Jim. "You're a growing boy."

But Freddy insisted. "My mom makes the best ham sandwiches, Jim."

"Thanks Freddy!"

"You're welcome, but I have to go now," said Freddy. "I'm going to find God today, so I can serve him. Take care, Jim."

By this time, Freddy was running out of ideas.

He couldn't find God on the hill,
        didn't see Him in the forest,
                and didn't see Him in the city.

Freddy wondered if God wanted to be found. He thought maybe he should give up and go home.

Just then Freddy had another thought, "Of course! I know!

"God must be at the hospital, helping people who are sick."

So, he ran straight for the hospital.

There were a lot of sick people waiting to see the doctor. Freddy was sure that God would be there, but he just couldn't find Him.

Sadly, Freddy left the hospital, but down the street, he saw...

a lady.

"Hi there, my name is Freddy. Are you okay?"
Freddy asked the lady.

"Hi Freddy," she said. "My name is Ruth. I hurt my
ankle today and I need to go into the hospital, but
I just can't walk any further."

"Let me help," said Freddy. Luckily, there was a wheelchair outside the hospital doors. Freddy ran to get the wheelchair and wheeled Ruth into the hospital.

"Thank you so much Freddy," said Ruth.

"You're welcome, but I have to go now. It's almost dinner time."

Freddy left the hospital and made his way back home.
He'd looked everywhere for God, but couldn't find Him anywhere.

When Freddy got home, his mother asked, "Did you find God today Freddy, and were you able to serve Him?"

"No," Freddy said with a frown, "I looked *everywhere...*"

"I looked on the hill. I looked in the forest. I went to the city and to the hospital. But I couldn't find God anywhere."

"Hmm," said Freddy's mother. "What else did you do today?"

"Well, I did meet some interesting people..."

Freddy told his mother about Leo - who was all alone, so they became friends.

And about his friend Sally - who was sick, so he gave her his jacket and walked her home.

Freddy told his mother about Jim - who was hungry, so he gave Jim his lunch.

And finally about Ruth - who could walk no further, so he helped her into the hospital.

"Freddy are you SURE you didn't find God and serve Him today?" his mother asked with a smile.

"I didn't *see* Him. I was looking for God ALL DAY!" Freddy said.

"You may not have *seen* God today Freddy, but by serving others, I think you may have *found* Him."

**Matthew 25:40b**
"Truly I tell you, whatever you did for one of the least of these brothers and sisters of mine, **you did for me**."